NIRVANA BASS

© 2007 by International Music Publications Ltd
First published by International Music Publications Ltd in 2007
International Music Publications Ltd is a Faber Music company
3 Queen Square, London WC1N 3AU

Guitar by Tom Fleming
Bass by Neil Williams
Drums by Noam Lederman
Mixed & Engineered by Dave Clarke
www.themewsrecordingstudios.com

Arranged by Neil Williams
Engraved by Tom Fleming
Edited by Lucy Holliday

Designed by Lydia Merrills-Ashcroft
Photo from Redferns Music Picture Library

Printed in England by Caligraving Ltd
All rights reserved

ISBN10: 0-571-52838-4
EAN13: 978-0-571-52838-7

To buy Faber Music publications or to find out about the full range of titles available,
please contact your local music retailer or Faber Music sales enquiries:

Faber Music Ltd, Burnt Mill, Elizabeth Way, Harlow, CM20 2HX England
Tel: +44(0)1279 82 89 82 Fax: +44(0)1279 82 89 83
sales@fabermusic.com fabermusic.com

ABOUT A GIRL

Words and Music by Kurt Cobain

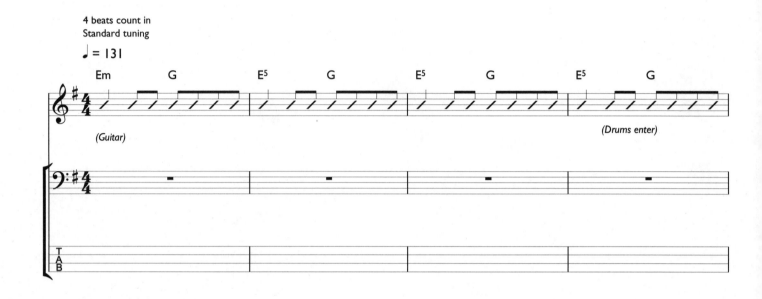

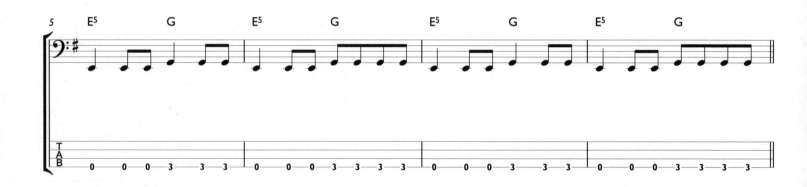

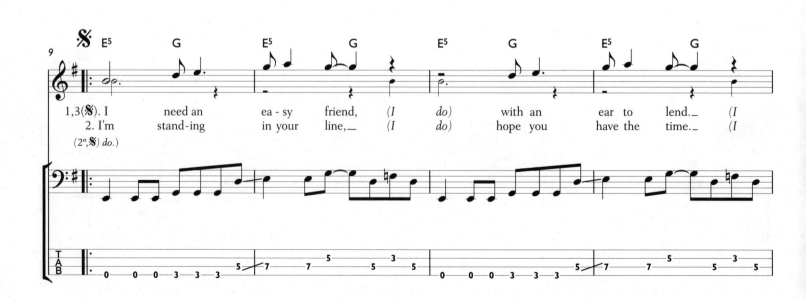

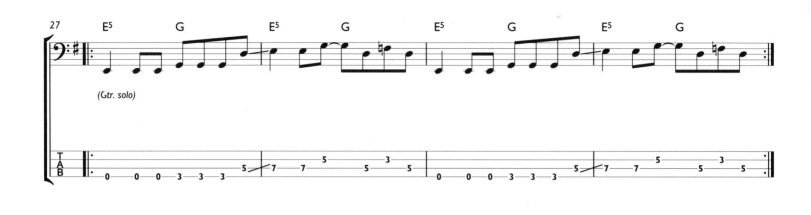

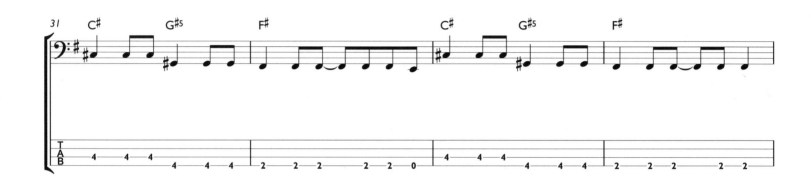

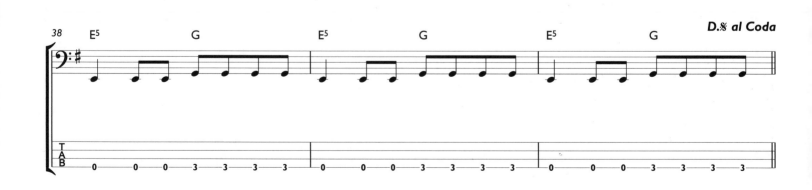

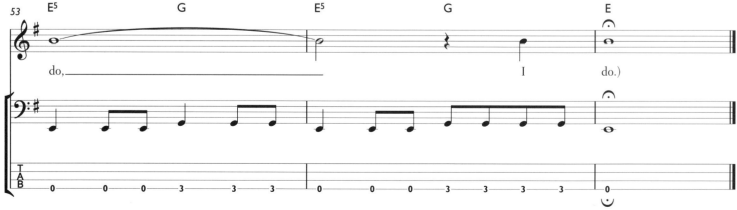

TRACK 3
BACKING TRACK 11

SMELLS LIKE TEEN SPIRIT

Words and Music by Kurt Cobain, Chris Novoselic and David Grohl

IN BLOOM

Words and Music by Kurt Cobain

4 beats count in
Standard tuning

♩ = 78

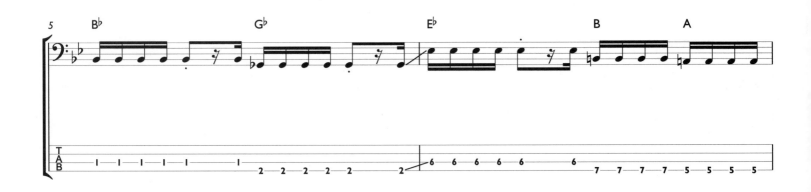

LITHIUM

Words and Music by Kurt Cobain

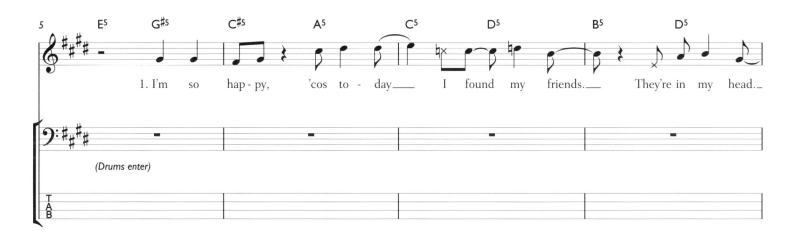

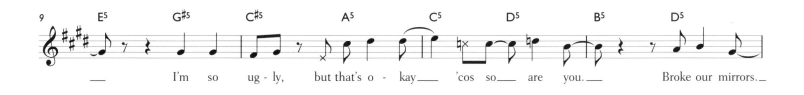

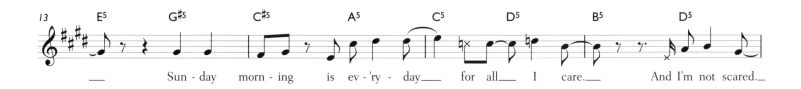

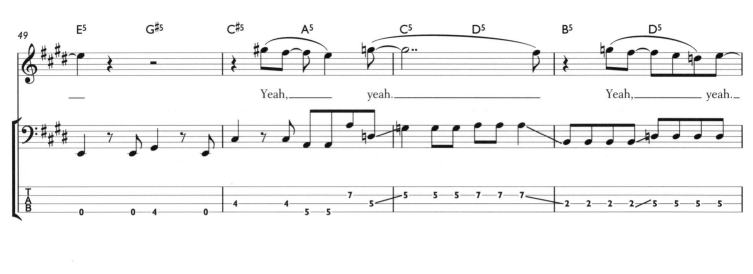

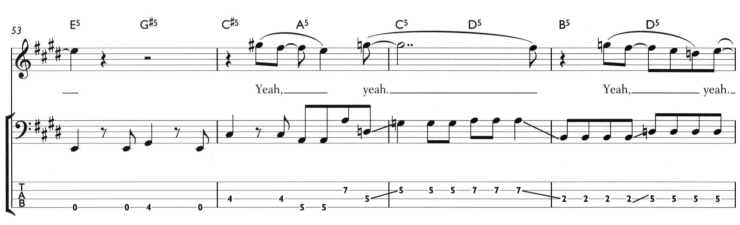

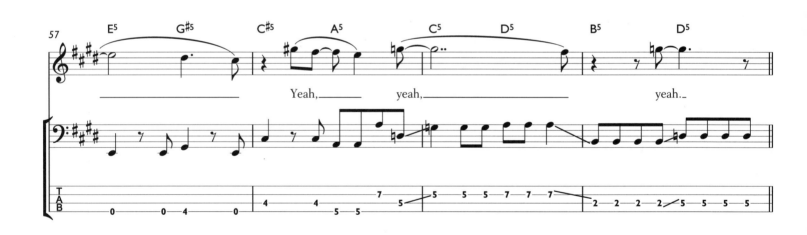

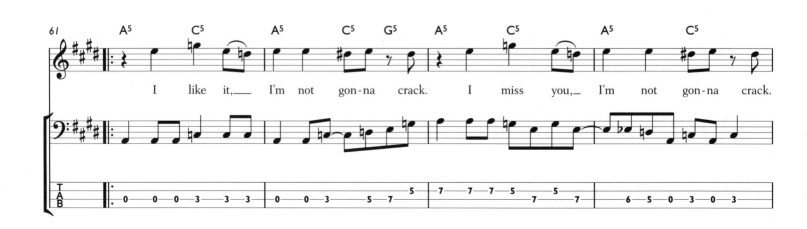

I love you,_ I'm not gon-na crack. I kill you,_ I'm not gon-na crack.

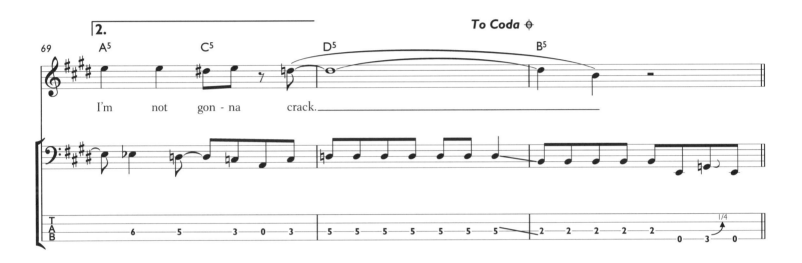

I'm not gon-na crack._____

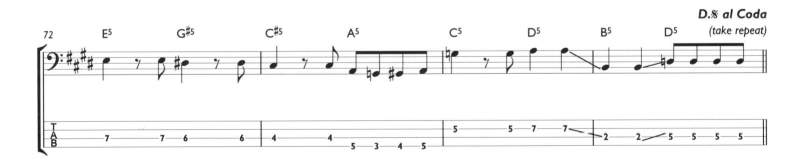

COME AS YOU ARE

Words and Music by Kurt Cobain

8 beats count in
Detune all strings
by a whole tone

♩ = 120

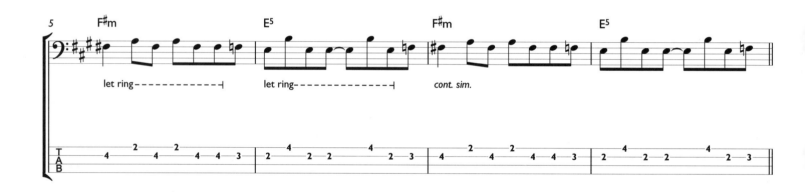

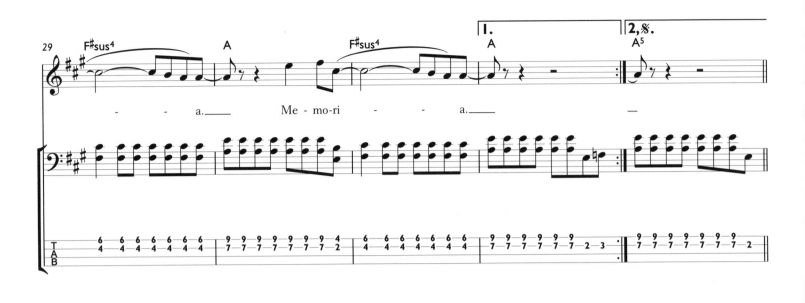

no I don't___ have a gun,___ no I don't___

___ have a gun,___ no I don't___ have a gun.___

TERRITORIAL PISSINGS

Words and Music by Kurt Cobain and Chet Powers

PENNY ROYAL TEA

Words and Music by Kurt Cobain

4 beats count in
Detune all strings
by a semitone
♩ = 114

1. I'm on ____ my time ____ with ev - 'ry - one, ____
3. I'm on ____ warm milk ____ and lax - a - tives, ____

I have ____ ve - ry ____ bad pos - ture. ____
Cher - ry ____ flav - ored ____ ant - a - cids. ____

I sit and drink ____ Pen-ny Roy-al tea, ____

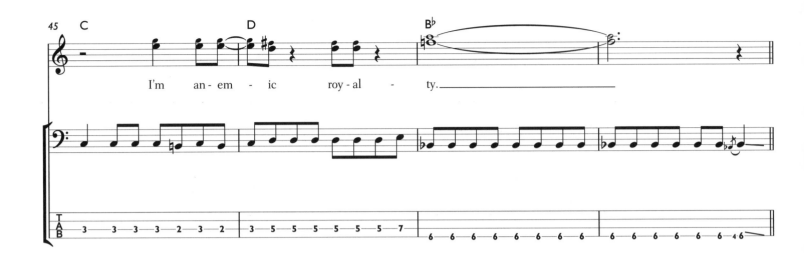

I'm an - em - ic roy - al - ty._____

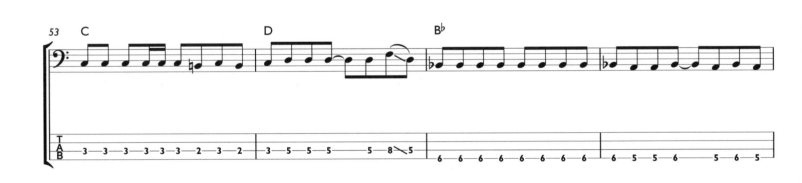

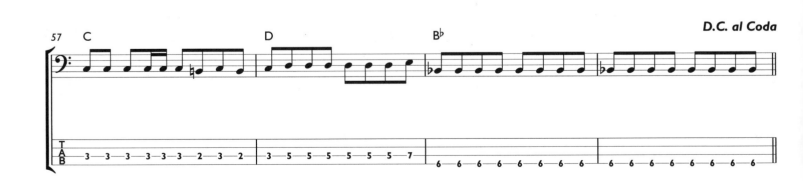

D.C. al Coda

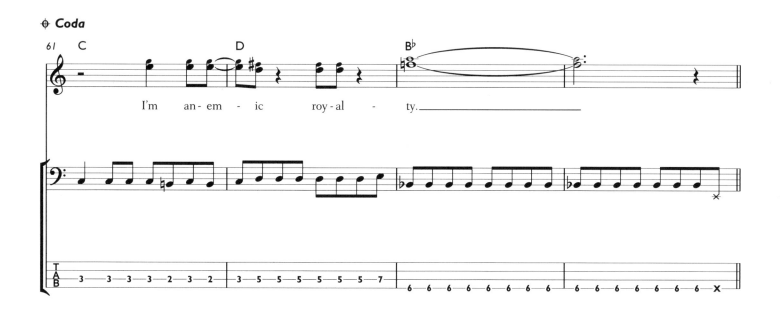

I'm an-em - ic roy-al - ty. _____

TRACK 9
BACKING TRACK 17

HEART-SHAPED BOX

Words and Music by Kurt Cobain

4 beats count in
Drop D tuning,
down a semitone.

♩ = 100

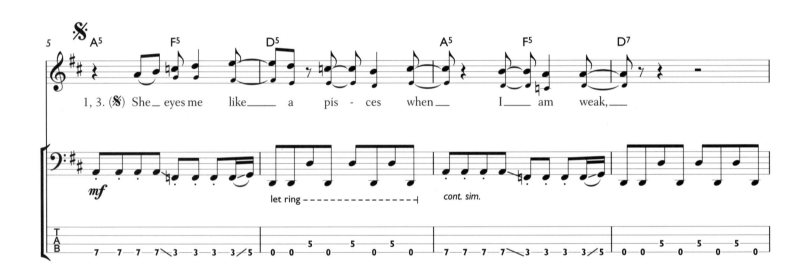

1, 3. (𝄋) She_ eyes me like_ a pis - ces when_ I_ am weak,_

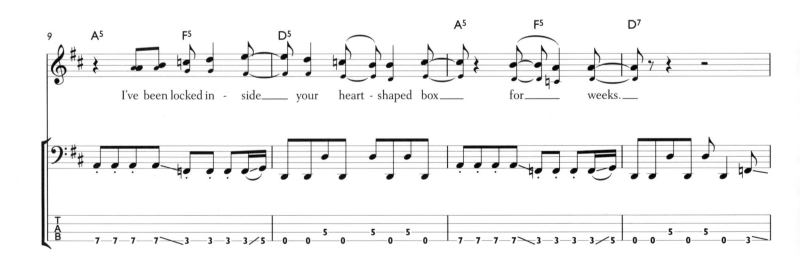

I've been locked in - side_ your heart - shaped box_ for_ weeks._

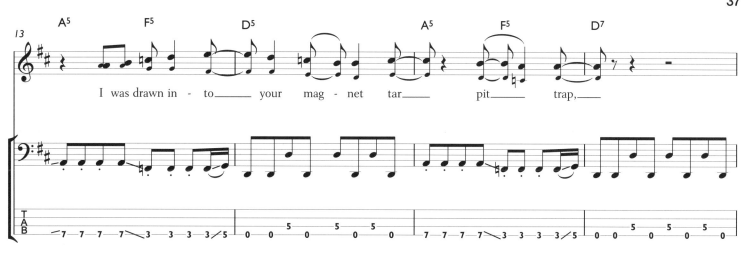

I was drawn in - to___ your mag - net tar___ pit___ trap,___

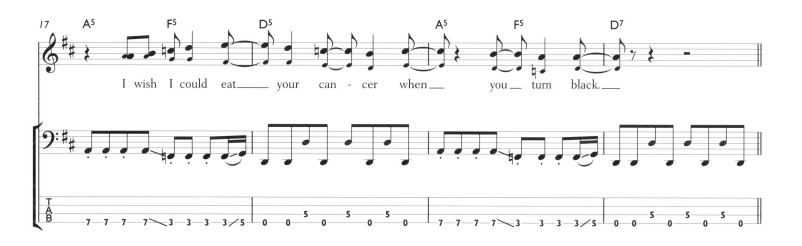

I wish I could eat___ your can - cer when___ you___ turn black.___

Hey! Wait! I've got a new com - plaint, for - ev - er in debt___ to your price - less ad - vice.

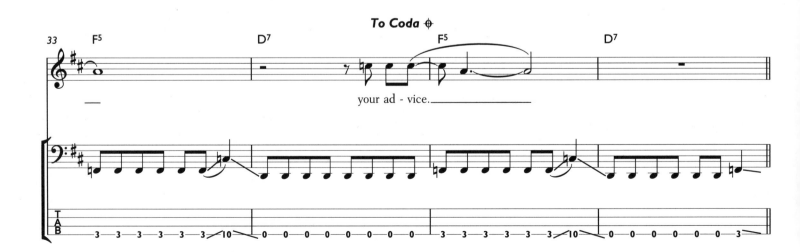

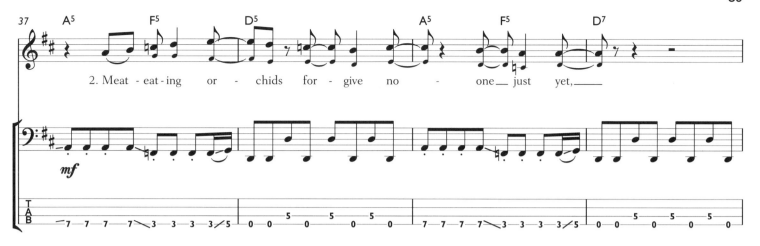

2. Meat-eat-ing or-chids for-give no - one__ just yet,____

cut my-self on an - gel's hair__ and ba - by's__ breath.__

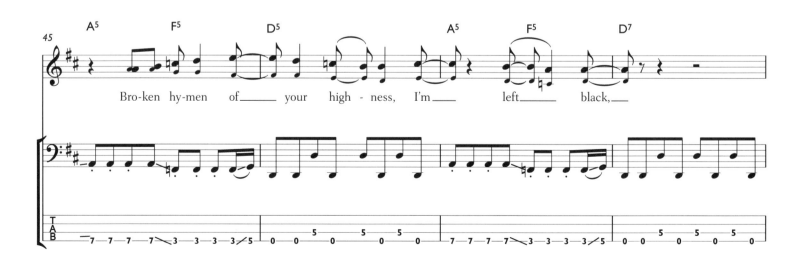

Bro-ken hy-men of____ your high - ness, I'm__ left____ black,__

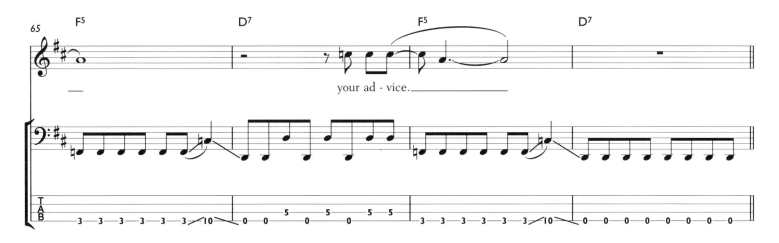

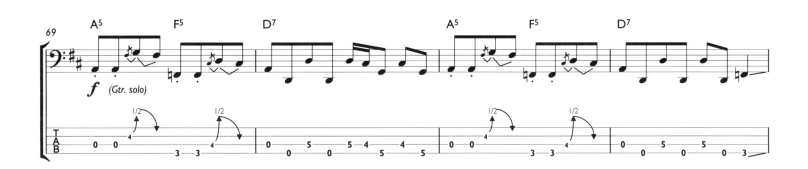

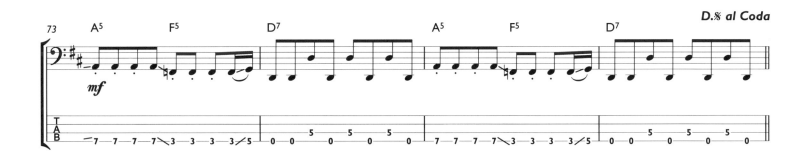

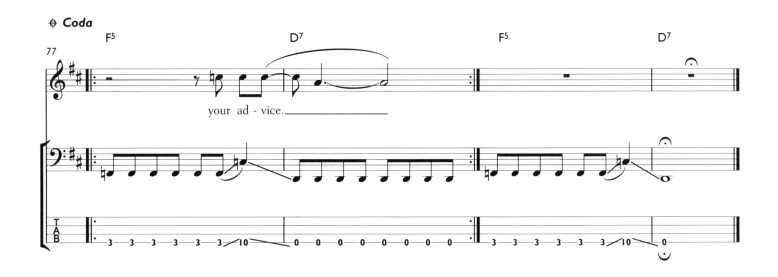

Notation and Tablature explained

Tuning your Bass

The best way to tune your bass is to use an electronic tuner.
Alternatively, you can use relative tuning—this will ensure that your bass is in tune with itself, but won't guarantee that you will be in tune with the original track (or any other musicians).

How to use relative tuning

Fret the low E string at the 5th fret and pluck—compare this with the sound of the open A string. The two notes should be in tune- if not, adjust the tuning of the A string until the two notes match.
Repeat this process for the other strings.

Detuning

If the song uses an unconventional tuning, it will say so clearly at the top of the music, e.g. 'detune bass down by a semitone' or '4 = D' (tune string 4 to D). The standard notation will always be in the key at which the song sounds, but the bass tab will take tuning changes into account. Just detune and follow the fret numbers.
The chord symbols will show the sounding chord above and the chord in which you are actually playing below in brackets.

Use of figures

In order to make the layout of scores clearer, figures that occur several times in a song will be numbered, e.g. 'Fig. 1', 'Fig. 2', etc.
A dotted line underneath shows the extent of the 'figure'. When the phrase is to be played, it will be marked clearly in the score, along with the instrument that should play it.

Reading Bass Tab

Bass tablature illustrates the four strings of the bass, graphically showing you where you put your fingers for each note or chord. It is always shown with a stave in standard musical notation above it. The bass tablature stave has four lines, each of them representing a different string. The top line is the high G string, the second line being the D string, and so on. Instead of using note heads, bass tab uses numbers which show the fret number to be stopped by the left hand. The rhythm is indicated underneath the tab stave. The example (below) shows four examples of single notes and two bass chords.

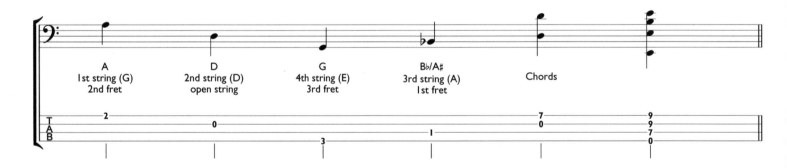

Notation of other bass techniques

Picking hand techniques:

1. Down and up strokes
These symbols show that the first and third notes are to be played with a down stroke of the pick and the others up strokes.

2. Palm mute
Mute the notes with the palm of the picking hand by lightly touching the strings near the bridge.

3. Pick rake
Drag the pick across the indicated strings with a single sweep. The extra pressure will often mute the notes slightly and accentuate the final note.

4. Arpeggiated chords
Strum across the indicated strings in the direction of the arrow head of the wavy line.

5. Tremolo picking
Shown by the slashes on the stem of the note. Very fast alternate picking. Rapidly and continuously move the pick up and down on each note.

6. Pick scrape
Drag the edge of the pick up or down the lower strings to create a scraping sound.

7. Slap techniques—tapping and popping
A 'T' means you tap or strike the string with your right-hand thumb. A 'P' means you 'pop' the string with your index or middle finger-pluck the string so hard that it falls back against the finger board with a slapping sound.

8. Right hand tapping
'Tap' onto the note indicated by a '+' with a finger of the picking hand. It is nearly always followed by a pull-off to sound the note fretted below.

9. Tap slide
As with tapping, but the tapped note is slid randomly up the fretboard, then pulled off to the following note.

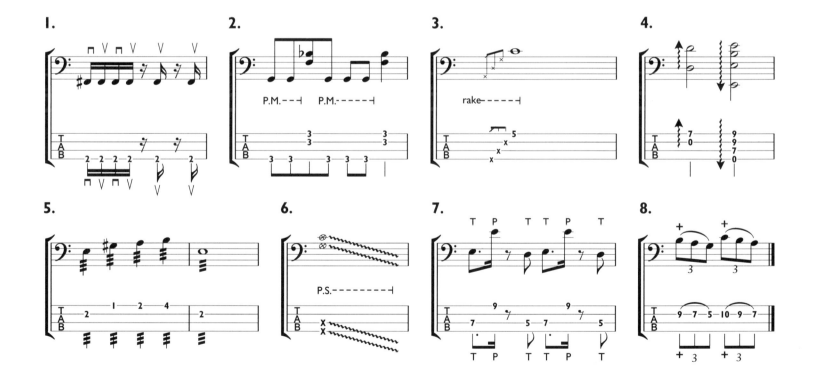

Fretting hand techniques:

1. Hammer-on and pull-off
These consist of two or more notes linked together by a slur. For hammer-ons, fret and play the lowest note, then 'hammer on' to the higher note with another finger. For a pull-off, play the highest note then 'pull off' to a lower note fretted with another finger. In both cases, only pick the first note.

2. Glissandi (slides)
Fret and pick the first note, then slide the finger up to the second note. If they are slurred together, do not re-pick the second note.

3. Slow glissando
Play the note(s) and slowly slide the finger(s) in the direction of the diagonal line(s).

4. Quick glissando
Play the note(s) and immediately slide the finger(s) in the direction of the diagonal line(s).

5. Trills
Play the note and rapidly alternate between this note and the nearest one above in the key signature. If a note in brackets is shown before, begin with this note.

6. Fret hand muting
Mute the notes with cross noteheads with the fretting hand.

7. Left hand tapping
Sound the note by tapping or hammering on to the note indicated by a 'o' with a finger of the fretting hand.

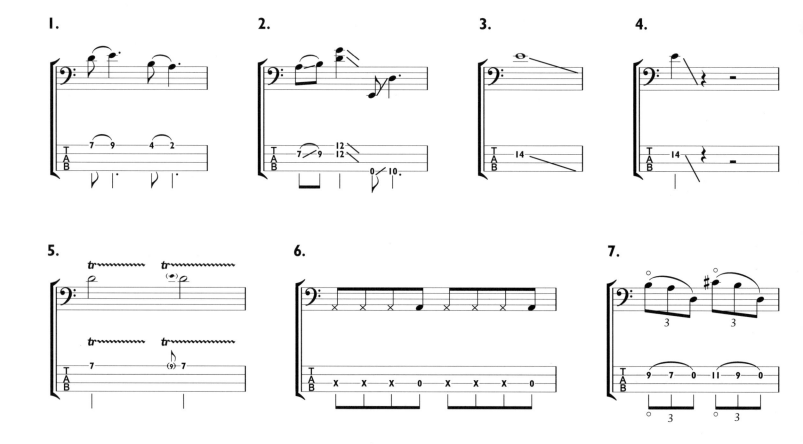

Bends and vibrato

Bends

Bends are shown by a curved arrow pointing to a number (in the tab).
Fret the first note and then bend the string up by the amount shown.

1. Semitone bend (half step bend)

The smallest conventional interval; equivalent to raising the note by
one fret.

2. Microtonal bend (quarter-tone bend, Blues curl)

Bend by a slight degree, roughly equivalent to half a fret.

3. Bend and release

Fret and pick the first note. Bend up for the length of the note
shown. May be followed by a release—letting the string fall back
down to the original pitch.

4. Ghost bend (prebend)

Fret the bracketed note and bend quickly before picking the note.

5. Reverse bend

Fret the bracketed note and bend quickly before picking the note,
immediately let fall back to the original.

6. Multiple bends

A series of bends and releases joined together. Only pick the
first note.

7. Vibrato

Shown by a wavy line. The fretting hand creates a vibrato effect
using small, rapid up and down bends.

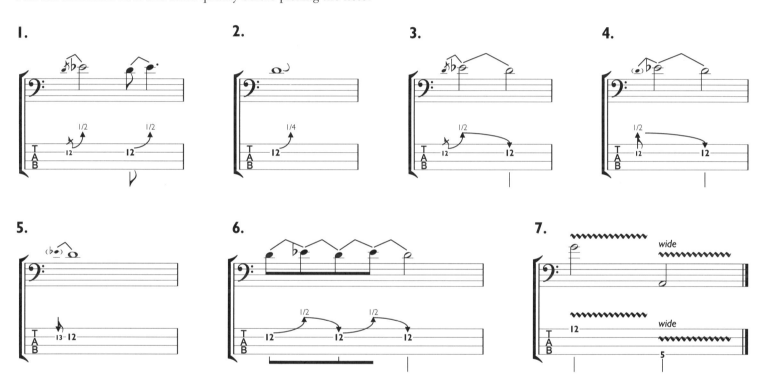

Harmonics & Other techniques

1. Natural harmonics

Instead of fretting properly, touch the string lightly with the fretting
hand at the fret shown in the tab. Pick as normal. Diamond
noteheads show the resultant pitch.

2. Artificial harmonics

The first tab number is fretted and held with the fretting hand as

normal. The picking hand then produces a harmonic by using a
finger to touch the string lightly at the fret shown by the bracketed
number. Pick with another finger of the picking hand.

3. Fingering (fretting hand)

Small numbers show the finger with which each note is to be
fretted.

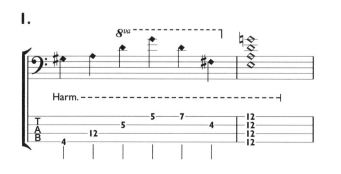

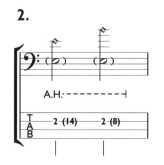

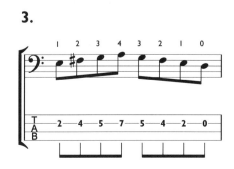

ISBN10:   0-571-52667-5
EAN13: 978-0-571-52667-3

PINK FLOYD
BASS

PLAY BASS GUITAR AND SING WITH PINK FLOYD! NINE OF THEIR GREATEST SONGS
TRANSCRIBED FOR BASS IN STANDARD NOTATION AND TABLATURE.
INCLUDES FANTASTIC SOUNDALIKE CDS.

To buy Faber Music publications or to find out about the full range of titles available
please contact your local music retailer or Faber Music sales enquiries:

Faber Music Ltd, Burnt Mill, Elizabeth Way, Harlow CM20 2HX
Tel: +44 (0) 1279 82 89 82   Fax: +44 (0) 1279 82 89 83
sales@fabermusic.com   fabermusic.com

ISBN10:   0-571-52546-6
EAN13: 978-0-571-52546-1